The Way Through the Woods

and other poems

Compiled by

John Foster

OXFORD

UNIVERSITY PRESS

OXFORD
UNIVERSITY PRESS

Great Clarendon Street, Oxford OX2 6DP

Oxford University Press is a department of the University of Oxford.
It furthers the University's objective of excellence in research, scholarship,
and education by publishing worldwide in

Oxford New York

Athens Auckland Bangkok Bogotá Buenos Aires Calcutta
Cape Town Chennai Dar es Salaam Delhi Florence Hong Kong Istanbul
Karachi Kuala Lumpur Madrid Melbourne Mexico City Mumbai
Nairobi Paris São Paulo Singapore Taipei Tokyo Toronto Warsaw

and associated companies in Berlin Ibadan

Oxford is a trade mark of Oxford University Press
in the UK and in certain other countries

British Library Cataloguing in Publication Data
Data available

ISBN 0 19 917285 4

Printed in Hong Kong

The editor and publisher would like to thank pupils of
Batt CE Primary School, Witney and Oxford High School Junior
Department for their help with comments on the poems.

The National Literacy Strategy termly requirements for poetry are
fulfilled on the following pages:

Term 1

pp 5, 14–32, 34–43, 60.

Term 2

pp 5–12, 54–59.

Term 3

pp 13–17, 21–22, 32–33, 38–39, 44–46, 52.

For more detailed information on the poetry range requirements
and the termly objectives, see Oxford Literacy Web Poetry
Teacher's Guide 1.

Contents

The Cockerel Proclaims

I am proud of my pride.
I open the doors of morning.
I shout the trees awake,
Circle your towns with a high
Magnificent, self-controlled cry.

One by one I snuff out the stars
And I am the first colours,
A reminder of the rainbow,
A singer shaming your small
Complaining voices. I'm tall

And proud of my flaring height.
I am the sun's true herald.
I wind up the small birds' voices.
And tell you it's worth getting up
As I lock the doors of the night.

Elizabeth Jennings

This bird thinks a
lot of itself!

Song to the Sun

The fearful night sinks
Trembling into the depth
Before your lightning eye
And the rapid arrows
From your fiery quiver
With sparking bows of light
You tear her cloak
The black cloak lined with fire
And studded with gleaming stars –
With sparking bows of light
You tear the black cloak.

Traditional African

I like this poem because I can
see the sun piercing the dark
sky with its rays.

Sun

Lightbringer
Joymaker
Nightchaser
Cloudshaker.

Foodgrower
Gloomfighter
Heatgiver
Moonlighter.

Sleepender
Icebreaker
Leafrouser
Plantwaker.

Skinbrowner
Nosepeeler
Feetwarmer
Hearthealer.

Steve Turner

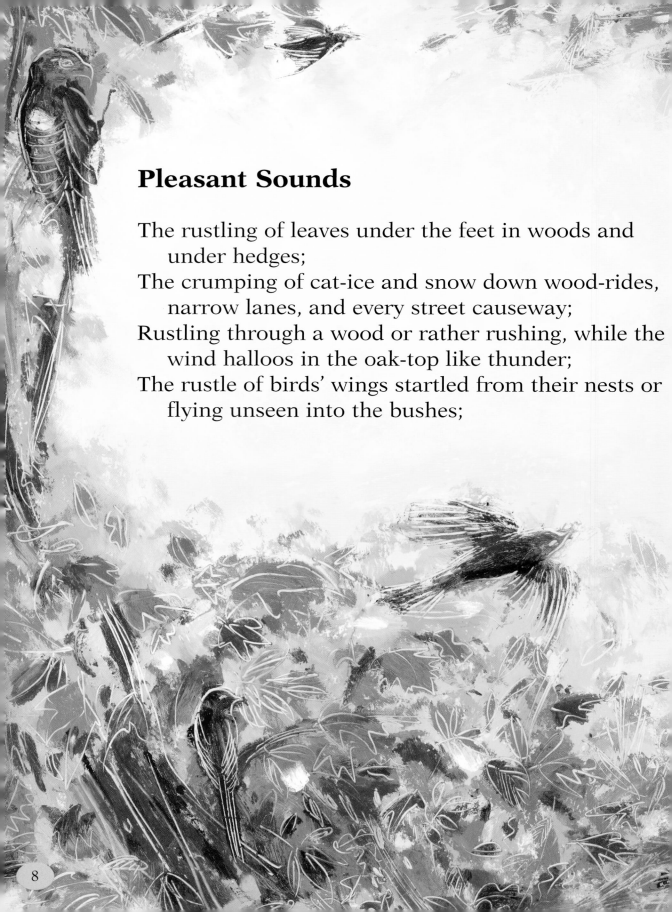

Pleasant Sounds

The rustling of leaves under the feet in woods and
    under hedges;
The crumping of cat-ice and snow down wood-rides,
    narrow lanes, and every street causeway;
Rustling through a wood or rather rushing, while the
    wind halloos in the oak-top like thunder;
The rustle of birds' wings startled from their nests or
    flying unseen into the bushes;

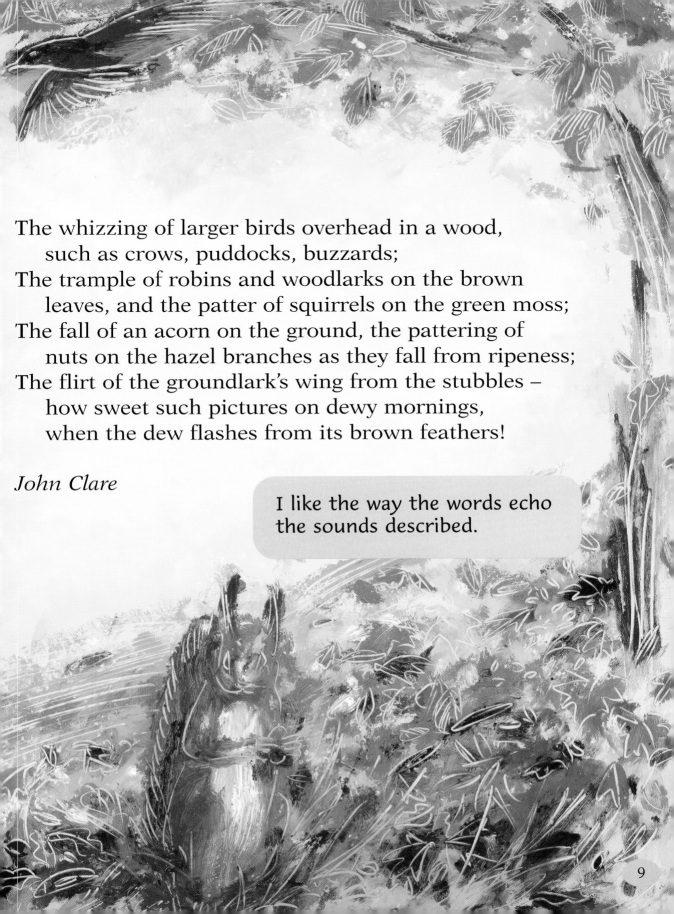

The whizzing of larger birds overhead in a wood,
    such as crows, puddocks, buzzards;
The trample of robins and woodlarks on the brown
    leaves, and the patter of squirrels on the green moss;
The fall of an acorn on the ground, the pattering of
    nuts on the hazel branches as they fall from ripeness;
The flirt of the groundlark's wing from the stubbles –
    how sweet such pictures on dewy mornings,
    when the dew flashes from its brown feathers!

John Clare

I like the way the words echo the sounds described.

9

The Storm

Without warning a snake of black
cloud rises in the sky.
It hisses as it runs and spreads its hood.
The moon goes out, the mountain is dark.
Far away is heard the shout of the demon.

Up rushes the storm a moment after
Rattling an iron chain in its teeth
The mountain suddenly lifts its
Trunks to the heavens
And the lake roars like a wild beast.

Ashok B Raha (translated by Lila Ray)

This poem is dark and fierce.

From Morning After a Storm

There was a roaring in the wind all night;
The rain came heavily and fell in floods;
But now the sun is rising calm and bright.
The birds are singing in the distant woods;
Over his own sweet voice the stock-dove broods.
The jay makes answer as the magpie chatters;
And all the air is filled with pleasant noise of waters.

William Wordsworth

from **The Brook**

I slip,
    I slide,
        I gloom,
            I glance,

    Among my skimming swallows;
I make the netted sunbeams dance
    Against my sandy shallows.

I murmur under moon and stars
    In brambly wildernesses;
I linger by my shingly bards;
    I loiter round my cresses;

And out again I curve and flow
    To join the brimming river,
For men may come and men may go,
    But I go on forever.

Alfred Lord Tennyson

I like the way the rhythm suggests how fast the stream is flowing.

Waterfall

Water, white as a veil,
Arches across rocks, falls,
Tosses in turbulent torrents,
Excites, enchants, enthralls.
Rushing and racing it roars, pours,
Furious and fast. Fantastic it spills.
Amazingly splintered it thrills.
Leaps, light-sparkling and lithe.
Lands and lingers in limpid, lace-edged pools.

Cynthia Rider

I can hear the waterfall tumble over the rocks.

Three Cinquains

Rainbow

Arching
through a black sky,
the colour of magic,
the gentle child of storm and sun
brings peace.

Lost

Falling,
spiralling down,
a bright coin vanishes
into watery depths to lie
unspent.

Space

The world
spins swiftly round.
Are we alone in space?
Is there anybody there?
Is there?

Marian Swinger

This makes me
wonder whether
there is.

Polar Bear

The secret of the polar bear
Is that he wears long underwear.

Gail Kredenser

The Orang-utan

The closest relative of man
They say, is the orang-utan;
And when I look at Grandpapa,
I realize how right they are.

Colin West

Glow-worm

I know a worried glow-worm,
I wonder what the matter is?
He seems so glum and gloomy,
Perhaps he needs new batteries.

Colin West

The Crocodile

The crocodile has a toothy smile.
He opens his jaws with a grin.
He's very polite.
Before taking a bite,
He always says, "Please come in!"

John Foster

The Woodland Haiku

Fox
Slinks to the wood's edge
and – with one paw raised – surveys
the open meadows.

Fallow Deer
Moving smooth as smoke
she starts at an air tremor.
Is gone like a ghost.

Rabbits
Blind panic sets in
and they're off, like dodgem cars
gone out of control.

Rooks
They float high above,
black as scraps of charred paper
drifting from a fire.

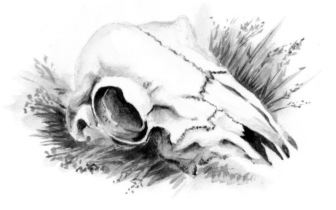

Owl

Blip on his radar
sends owl whooshing through the dark,
homing in on rats, mice.

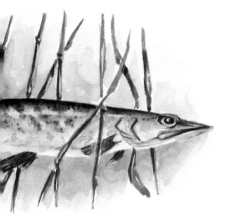

Pike

Killer submarine
he lurks deep in the woodland's
green-skinned pond. Lurks…strikes.

Sheep's Skull

Whitened and toothless,
discovered in a damp ditch.
A trophy for home.

Humans

Clumsy, twig-snapping,
they see nothing but trees, trees.
The creatures hide…watch…

Wes Magee

Mother's Day

Dear God,
Today is Mother's Day,
Please may her back ache go
away.

May her pot plants all grow
healthy
and a win on the lottery make
her wealthy.

May our dad buy her some
flowers
and take us all to Alton
Towers.

May her fruitcake always rise
and the sun shine bright
in her blue skies.

Roger Stevens

This poem made me think
about my mum.

My Dad, Your Dad

My dad's fatter than your dad,
Yes, my dad's fatter than yours:
If he eats any more he won't fit in the house,
He'll have to live out of doors.

Yes, but my dad's balder than your dad,
My dad's balder, OK?
He's only got two hairs left on his head
And both are turning grey.

Ah, but my dad's thicker than your dad,
My dad's thicker, all right,
He has to look at his watch to see
If it's noon or the middle of the night.

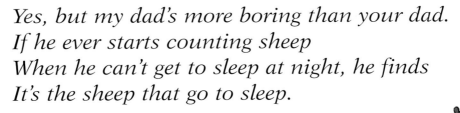

Yes, but my dad's more boring than your dad.
If he ever starts counting sheep
When he can't get to sleep at night, he finds
It's the sheep that go to sleep.

But my dad doesn't mind your dad.
Mine quite likes yours too.
I suppose they don't always think much of US!
That's true, I suppose, that's true.

Kit Wright

21

Fair's Fair

When my little sister
Comes into my room,
I tell her to go.

"No," she says.
"I don't have to."

"If you don't," I say,
"I'll tell Mum."

"It's a free world," she says.

"Well, if it's a free world,
I'll go and play in your room."

It always works.

"It's not fair," she shouts,
As she stamps out.

June Crebbin

This made me smile
because it's exactly what
happens at my house.

Granny

Granny is
fried dumplin' an' run-rung,
coconut drops an' grater cake,
fresh-ground coffee smell in the mornin'
when we wake.

Granny is
loadin' up the donkey
basket full up on market day
with fresh snapper the fishermen bring back
from the bay.

Granny is
clothes washin' in the river
scrubbin' dirt out on the stone
haulin' crayfish an' eel from water
on her own.

Granny is
stories in the moonlight
underneath the guango tree
and a spiderweb of magic
all round we.

Granny say
all the best for the gran'children
it no matter what the price
don't want no one pointin' finger.

Granny nice.

Valerie Bloom

My Granny's nice too!

25

Gran Can You Rap?

Gran was in her chair she was taking a nap
When I tapped her on the shoulder to see if she could rap.
Gran, can you rap? Can you rap? Can you, Gran?
And she opened one eye and said to me, man,
    I'm the best rapping Gran this world's ever seen
    I'm a tip-top, slip-slap, rap-rap queen.

And she rose from her chair in the corner of the room
And she started to rap with a bim-bam-boom,
And she rolled up her eyes and she rolled round her head
And as she rolled by this is what she said,
    I'm the best rapping Gran this world's ever seen
    I'm a nip-nap, yip-yap, rap-rap queen.

Then she rapped past my dad and she rapped past my mother,
She rapped past me and my little baby brother.
She rapped her arms narrow she rapped her arms wide,
She rapped through the door and she rapped outside.
  She's the best rapping Gran this world's ever seen
  She's a drip-drop, trip-trap, rap-rap queen.

She rapped down the garden she rapped down the street,
The neighbours all cheered and they tapped their feet.
She rapped through the traffic lights as they turned red
As she rapped round the corner this is what she said,
  I'm the best rapping Gran this world's ever seen
  I'm a flip-flop, hip-hop, rap-rap queen.

She rapped down the lane she rapped up the hill,
And as she disappeared she was rapping still.
I could hear Gran's voice saying, Listen, man,
Listen to the rapping of the rap-rap Gran.

    I'm the best rapping Gran this world's ever seen
    I'm a –
    tip-top, slip-slap,
        nip-nap, yip-yap,
            hip-hop, trip-trap,
                touch yer cap,
                  take a nap,
                      happy, happy, happy, happy,
                        rap-rap-queen.

Jack Ousbey

I wish my Gran could rap!

My Sparrow Gran

My sparrow gran
Is the singing one
Busy and tidy
And brown-bright-eyed
She chirrups and chats
She scurries and darts
She picks up the bits
That clutter her nest
And when evening comes
When all her work's done
I bring her my book
And sit on her lap
Snug in her arms
That are feather-down-warm.

Berlie Doherty

Grandpa

Grandpa's hands are as rough as garden sacks
And as warm as pockets.
His skin is crushed paper round his eyes
Wrapping up their secrets.

Berlie Doherty

My Grandpa has
hands like this.

Grandad's Face was a Picture

Grandad's face was a picture
On his birthday.
When Mum gave him a new camera.
He spent the rest of the day
Pestering people to pose for him.

Grandad's face was a picture
In the evening
When he opened up the camera
And found he'd forgotten
To put in a film.

John Foster

Uncle

Uncle, whose inventive brains
Kept evolving aeroplanes,
Fell from an enormous height
On my garden lawn, last night.
Flying is a fatal sport.
Uncle wrecked the tennis court.

Harry Graham

Cousin Nell

Cousin Nell
married a frogman
in the hope
that one day
he would turn into
a handsome prince.

Instead he turned into
a sewage pipe
near Gravesend
and was never seen again.

Roger McGough

The Termite

Some primal termite knocked on wood
And tasted it, and found it good,
And that is why your cousin May
Fell through the parlour floor today.

Ogden Nash

There was a Young Lady of Lynn

There was a young lady of Lynn
Who was so uncommonly thin
That when she essayed
To drink lemonade,
She slipped through the straw and fell in.

Anon

I Hear

When I think of school I hear
High shouts tossed
Like juggled balls in windy yards, and lost
In gutters, treetops, air,
and always, somewhere,
Piano notes waterfall
And small sharp voices wail.
A monster-roar surges – GOAL!
The bell.

Then doors slam.
There's the kick, scuff, stamp of shoes
Down corridors that trap and trail echoes.
Desk-tops thud with books, kit-bags.
A child's ghost screams as her chair's pushed back.
Laughter bubbles up and bursts.
Screech-owl whistles, quick-fox quarrel flares,
The voice barks QUIET!

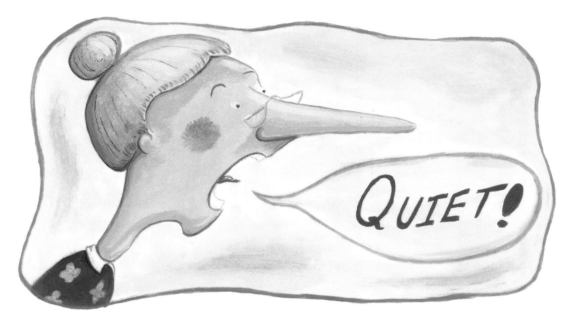

All sit. All wait.
Till scraped chalk shrieks
And whispers creep,
Cough. Ruler crack. Desk creak.

And furtive into the silence comes
A tiny mouse-scrabbling of pens.
Scamper. Stop, Scamper. Stop. Tiptoe.

And there, just outside the top window
As if it had never ceased to be
But only needed listening to
A scatter of birdsong, floating free.

Berlie Doherty

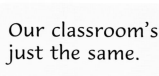

Our classroom's
just the same.

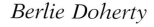

Recipe for Playtime

Ingredients

1 bell
6 carefully selected friends (to mix with)
2 to be left out as they might spoil the mixture
15 teacher-free minutes
1 handful of ideas
Mixed fruit, sweets or crisps (for sharing)
Noise to taste

Method

1 Look at the clock when working.
2 Wait for the bell to ring.
3 Dash to your favourite tree trunk.
4 Hide from your friends, then S P R I N G!
5 Roll down the hill in freedom.
6 Decide who'll be in for tig.
7 Shout for your favourite leader.
8 Stand on your head, then dig!
9 Do all the things you want to,
10 Instead of the things they say.
11 Enjoy all the thrills of playtime,
12 And turn out for more next day!

This recipe should be used three times
daily in order to ensure freshness.

Daphne Kitching

Maths

What do you minus
and from where?
I ask my teacher
but he don't care.

Ten cubic metres
in square roots,
or how many toes
go in nine boots?

Change ten decimals
to a fraction.
AaaaaaaaaaaaaaaahhhhhhhhhhhhhhhH!
Is my reaction.

Deepak Kahla

This is how I feel
in Maths lessons.

Names

They call you names for the fun of it,
To make your insides weak,
To injure all of your happiness
And tell you you're a SIKH.

To them you're totally different,
To them you're Lower Class,
They'll hit you and hurt you as much as they can
Till your insides are eaten at last.

They say that you're brown and they hate you,
And they never ever go away,
They've become part of your life now,
And I fear that they're here to stay.

Kirandeep Chahal

Four o'clock Friday

Four o'clock Friday, I'm home at last,
Time to forget the week that's past.
On Monday, in break they stole my ball
And threw it over the playground wall.
On Tuesday afternoon, in games
They threw mud at me and called me names.
On Wednesday, they trampled my books on the floor,
So Miss kept me in because I swore.
On Thursday, they laughed after the test
'Cause my marks were lower than the rest.
Four o'clock Friday, at last I'm free,
For two whole days they can't get at me.

John Foster

This captures just what
it's like to be bullied.

Tiger in a Zoo

She stalks a steel-branched jungle
And paces concrete grass,
Though her stripes afford poor camouflage
Behind the metal bars.

She paces concrete grass
And sees the horizon shimmer
As against the city's drizzle,
The distant mountains glimmer.

She sees the horizon shimmer
Beneath an uncaged sky
And hunts a shadow antelope
As spectral vultures fly.

Beneath an uncaged sky
My imagination stirs
But the zoo is her world
And has always been;
And the dreams are mine
Not hers.

Pat Moon

New Town

Birds don't sing where we live any more.
The Council rooted up the trees there used to be before,
Elder and sycamore and hazel and birch.
There's nowhere in our district for the birds to perch.

The Council laid down concrete roads and made up
    woody names,
Grove Lane and Copse Hill and that kind of thing.
All right for traffic and cross-last games
But there's nowhere for the birds to build their nests
    and sing.

Sparrows didn't mind and pigeons didn't mind.
They're the only sort left; they stayed behind.
But blackbirds and chaffinches and wrens are gone
    for good.
You don't hear them sing now in our neighbourhood.

Joan Aiken

Graveyard Scene

There are no names on the gravestones now,
They've been washed away by the rain.
The graveyard trees are skeletons now,
They will never wear leaves again.

Instead of a forest the tower surveys
A bleak and desolate plain.
Those are not tears in the gargoyle's eyes,
They are droplets of acid rain.

John Foster

I like the strong message in this poem.

Epitaphs

Here lies a careless boy named Gunn
Who fed a lion with a bun.
At least, in one hand held a bun
But, typically, fed the other one.

A man called Percy Brown lies here
Who used to sip his father's beer.
And later on he sipped his own:
His weight at death was forty stone.

Here lies a greedy girl, Jane Bevan,
Whose breakfasts hardly ever stopped.
One morning at half past eleven
She snapped and crackled and then popped.

A schoolmistress called Binks lies here.
She held her own for twenty year.
She pleaded, biffed, said: "I'm your friend."
But children got her in the end.

Here lies Prue Jones, whose childish folly
Was to eat too much of a lime iced lolly
And get a splinter in a place
Where splinters make a hopeless case.

Here lies John Smith, exactly eight,
Who was given a handsome chemistry set.
Here also lies his sister, Maria.
Or what was left of them after the fire.

Here lies Amanda Mary Wilde
Who was in fact a lying child.
Her end came as she told a whopper
While sucking a two-penny gob-stopper.

Here lies a family dog called Rover:
His pampered life at last is over.
On Rover more than on each other
Love was bestowed by Dad and Mother.

Here lies a precocious, insomniac tot
Who knew how to let down the side of his cot.
He undid the catches one evening at seven
And, the bars having vanished, fell straight up to heaven.

Roy Fuller

Ghost in the Garden

The ghost in the garden
Cracks twigs as she treads
Shuffles the leaves
But isn't there

The ghost in the garden
Snaps back the brambles
So they spring against my legs
But isn't there

Draws spiders' webs across my face
Breathes mist on my cheek
Whispers with bird-breath down my ear
But isn't there

Tosses raindrops down from branches
Splashes the pond
Traces a face in it
That isn't mine

Moves shadows underneath the trees
Too tall, too thin, too tiny to be me

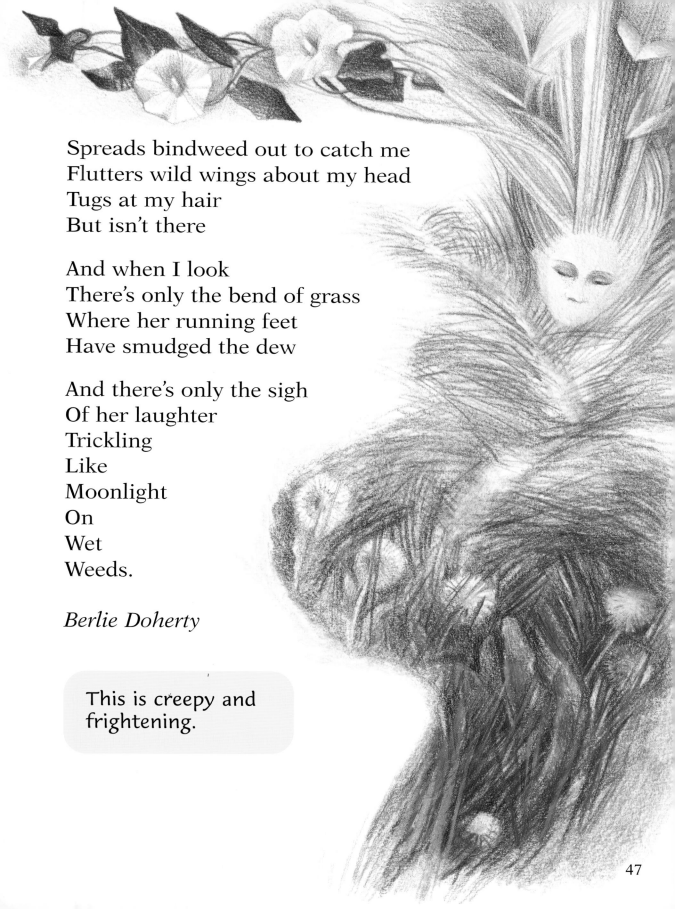

Spreads bindweed out to catch me
Flutters wild wings about my head
Tugs at my hair
But isn't there

And when I look
There's only the bend of grass
Where her running feet
Have smudged the dew

And there's only the sigh
Of her laughter
Trickling
Like
Moonlight
On
Wet
Weeds.

Berlie Doherty

This is creepy and
frightening.

The Way Through the Woods

They shut the road through the woods
    Seventy years ago.
Weather and rain have undone it again,
    And now you would never know
There was once a road through the woods
    Before they planted the trees.

It is underneath the coppice and heath,
    And the thin anemones.
    Only the keeper sees
That, where the ring-dove broods,
    And the badgers roll at ease,
There was once a road through the woods.

Yet, if you enter the woods
    Of a summer evening late,
When the night-air cools on the trout-ringed pools
    Where the otter whistles his mate,
(They fear not men in the woods,
    Because they see so few)
You will hear the beat of a horse's feet
    And the swish of a skirt in the dew,
    Steadily cantering through
The misty solitudes,
    As though they perfectly knew
The old lost road through the woods...
But there is no road through the woods.

Rudyard Kipling

I like this poem because it's mysterious.

What Has Happened to Lulu?

What has happened to Lulu, mother?
    What has happened to Lu?
There's nothing in her bed but an old rag-doll
    And by its side a shoe.

Why is her window wide, mother,
    The curtain flapping free,
And only a circle on the dusty shelf
    Where her money-box used to be?

Why do you turn your head, mother,
    And why do the tear-drops fall?
And why do you crumple that note on the fire
    And say it is nothing at all?

I woke to voices late last night,
    I heard an engine roar.
Why do you tell me the things I heard
    Were a dream and nothing more?

I heard somebody cry, mother,
    In anger or in pain,
But now I ask you why, mother,
    You say it was a gust of rain.

Why do you wander about as though
    You don't know what to do?
What has happened to Lulu, mother?
    What has happened to Lu?

Charles Causley

I wonder, what did happen to Lulu?

The Magic Box

I will put in the box

the swish of silk sari on a summer night,
fire from the nostrils of a Chinese dragon,
the tip of a tongue touching a tooth.

I will put in the box

a snowman with a rumbling belly,
a sip of the bluest water from Lake Lucerne,
a leaping spark from an electric fish.

I will put in the box

three violet wishes spoken in Gujarati,
the last joke of an ancient uncle
and the first smile of a baby.

I will put in the box

a fifth season and a black sun,
a cowboy on a broomstick
and a witch on a white horse.

My box is fashioned from ice and gold and steel,
with stars on the lid and secrets in the corners.
Its hinges are the toe joints of dinosaurs.

I shall surf in my box
on the great high-rolling breakers of the wild Atlantic,
then wash ashore on a yellow beach
the colour of the sun.

Kit Wright

What a strange and wonderful box!

What are Heavy? Sea-Sand and Sorrow

What are heavy? Sea-sand and sorrow:
What are brief? Today and tomorrow:
What are frail? Spring blossoms and youth:
What are deep? The ocean and truth.

Christina Rossetti

This makes me feel sad.

Swift Things are Beautiful

Swift things are beautiful:
Swallows and deer,
And lightning that falls
Bright veined and clear,
Rivers and meteors,
Wind in the wheat,
The strong-withered horse,
The runner's sure feet.

And slow things are beautiful:
The closing of day,
The pause of the wave
That curves downward to spray,
The ember that crumbles,
The opening flower,
And the ox that moves on
In the quiet of power.

Elizabeth Coatsworth

Opposites

As hot as the dusty wind that blows across the desert,
As cold as a witch's stare.

As hard as a pat on the back by a giant,
As soft as a handshake with a delicate petal.

As slow as the white clouds going inch by inch across the sky,
As fast as a dolphin speeding under the water.

As wet as a snail's trail as it slithers down the path,
As dry as a chunk of bread left out in the sun.

As smooth as the voice of a confident villain,
As rough as the growl of an angry dog.

Graeme Walker

Quietly

Quietly the fox stalks its prey.
Quietly the cat sleeps in the hay.
Quietly the man sits in his chair.
Quietly the mermaid combs her hair.

Quietly the swan glides down the river.
Quietly the snake begins to slither.
Quietly moves the moon – but most quiet of all
Is the thinking I've done watching leaves fall.

Aenaone Tucker

(dedicated to her grandmother)

This poem makes me feel calm and peaceful.

Still the Dark Forest

Still the dark forest, quiet the deep,
Softly the clock ticks, baby must sleep!
The pole star is shining, bright the Great Bear,
Orion is watching, high up in the air.

Reindeer are coming to drive you away
Over the snow on an ebony sleigh,
Over the mountain and over the sea
You shall go happy and handsome and free.

Over the green grass pasture there
You shall go hunting the beautiful deer,
You shall pick flowers, the white and the blue,
Shepherds shall flute their sweetest for you.

And in the castle tower above,
The princess' cheeks burn red for your love,
You shall be king and queen of the land,
Happy for ever, hand in hand.

W H Auden

I can imagine someone singing
this poem to a child.

58

The Tide Rises, the Tide Falls

The tide rises, the tide falls,
The twilight darkens, the curlew calls;
Along the sea sands damp and brown
The traveller hastens towards the town,
    And the tide rises, the tide falls.

Darkness settles on roofs and walls
But the sea, the sea in the darkness calls;
The little waves, with their soft, white hands,
Efface the footprints in the sands
    And the tide rises, the tide falls.

The morning breaks; the steeds in their stalls
Stamp and neigh, as the hostler calls;
The day returns, but nevermore
Returns the traveller to the shore,
    And the tide rises, the tide falls.

Henry Wadsworth Longfellow

I can feel the waves when I read this poem.

The Last Day

If this were the last day
I ever would spend,
I'd find a sad person
And make him my friend.

I'd tell him a story,
I'd sing him a song,
I'd go for a walk
And I'd take him along.

I'd tell him a story
Of rivers and seas
And mountains so high
That they do not have trees.

But castles of ice
That sparkle and glow
And a fine mist of clouds
And a powder of snow.

I'd sing him a song
Of a place far away
Where for months it is night
And for months it is day

And colourful curtains
Of dazzling light
Dance over the skies
In the months of the night.

In the months of the day
We would walk, he and I,
To the place where the line
Of the sea meets the sky.

We would play with the fishes
And ride on the waves
And visit the oysters
Deep down in their caves

And they'd tell us fine stories
My good friend and me
And we'd smile at the sun
And talk to the sea.

Pamela Mordecai

What a magical way to
spend the last day.

Index of First Lines

Acknowledgements

The editor and publisher are grateful for permission to include the following poems:

Joan Aiken: 'New Town', an extract from 'A Leaf in the Shape of a Key', from *The Last Slice of Rainbow* (Jonathan Cape); **W H Auden:** 'Still the Dark Forest', from *The Ascent of F6* by W H Auden and Christopher Isherwood (Faber and Faber Ltd), reprinted by permission of the publisher; **Valerie Bloom:** 'Granny', © Valerie Bloom 2000, first published in this collection by permission of the author; **Charles Causley:** 'What Has Happened to Lulu?' from *Collected Poems for Children* by Charles Causley (Macmillan Publishers), reprinted by permission of David Higham Associates Ltd; **Kirandeep Chahal:** 'Names', from *The Hillingdon NAPE Journal*, Spring 1985; **John Clare:** 'Pleasant Sounds', from *Selected Poems and Prose of John Clare* edited by Eric Robinson and Geoffrey Summerfield (OUP, 1967), © Eric Robinson 1967, reprinted by permission of Curtis Brown Ltd on behalf of Eric Robinson; **Elizabeth Coatsworth:** 'Swift Things are Beautiful' (Macmillan Publishing Co), 1934 by Macmillan Publishing Co, © renewed 1962, reprinted by permission of C Beston Barnes; **June Crebbin:** 'Fair's Fair', from *The Dinosaur's Dinner* (Viking, 1992), © June Crebbin 1992, reprinted by permission of the author; **Berlie Doherty:** 'My Sparrow Gran', 'Grandpa', 'I Hear' and 'Ghost in the Garden', from *Walking on Air* (HarperCollins), reprinted by permission of David Higham Associates Ltd; **John Foster:** 'Four o'clock Friday' and 'Graveyard Scene', both © John Foster 1991, first published in *Four o'clock Friday* (OUP, 1991), 'Grandad's Face was a Picture", © John Foster 1997, first published in *Making Waves* (OUP, 1997), 'Crocodile', © John Foster 2000, first published in this collection, all reprinted by permission of the author; **Roy Fuller:** 'Epitaphs', from *The World Through the Window* (Blackie), © John Fuller, reprinted by permission of John Fuller; **Elizabeth Jennings:** 'The Cockerel Proclaims' from *A Spell of Words* by Elizabeth Jennings (Macmillan Publishing), reprinted by permission of David Higham Associates; **Rudyard Kipling:** 'The Way Through the Woods' from *Rewards and Fairies*, reprinted by permission of A P Watt Ltd on behalf of The National Trust for Places of Historic Interest or Natural Beauty; **Daphne Kitching:** 'Recipe for Playtime', © Daphne Kitching 2000, first published in this collection by permission of the author; **Wes Magee:** 'The Woodland Haiku', © Wes Magee 2000, first published in this collection by permission of the author; **Roger McGough:** 'Cousin Nell', from *Sporting Relations* (Eyre Methuen), reprinted by permission of The Peters Fraser and Dunlop Group Limited on behalf of Roger McGough; **Pat Moon:** 'Tiger in a Zoo', © Pat Moon 2000, first published in this collection by permission of the author; **Pamela Mordecai:** 'The Last Day', first published in *Ezra's Goldfish and Other Story Poems* (National Book Development Council of Jamaica, 1995), © Pamela Mordecai 1995, reprinted by permission of the author; **Ogden Nash:** 'The Termite', from *Verses from 1929 On* (Little Brown & Co, 1942), also from *Candy Is Dandy: The Best of Ogden Nash* (Andre Deutsch) reprinted by permission of Curtis Brown Limited, New York, and Andre Deutsch Ltd; **Jack Ousbey:** 'Gran Can You Rap?', © Jack Ousbey 2000, first published in this collection by permission of the author; **Cynthia Rider:** 'Waterfall', © Cynthia Rider 2000, first published in this collection by permission of the author; **Roger Stevens:** 'Mother's Day", © Roger Stevens 2000, first published in this collection by permission of the author; **Marian Swinger:** 'Three Cinquains', © Marian Swinger 2000, first published in this collection by permission of the author; **Aenaone Tucker:** 'Quietly', first published in *Words from the Middle* (OUP), reprinted by permission of the author; **Steve Turner:** 'Sun', from *The Day I Fell Down the Toilet and Other Poems* (Lion Publishing), reprinted by permission of the publisher; **Graeme Walker:** 'Opposites', © Graeme Walker 2000, first published in this collection by permission of the author; **Colin West:** 'The Orang-utan', © Colin West 1984, first published in *It's Funny When You Look at It* (Hutchinson, 1984), 'Glow-worm', © Colin West 1982, first published in *Not to be Taken Seriously* (Hutchinson, 1982), both reprinted by permission of the author; **Kit Wright:** 'The Magic Box', from *Cat Among the Pigeons* (Viking Kestrel, 1987), © Kit Wright 1984, 1987, reprinted by permission of Penguin Books Limited; 'My Dad, Your Dad' from *Rabbitting On* (HarperCollins), reprinted by permission of the author.

Although we have tried to trace and contact holders before publication, in some cases this has not been possible. If contacted we will be pleased to rectify any errors or omissions at the earliest opportunity.

The Artists

Anni Axworthy pp 44–45;
Peter Bailey pp 40–41;
Alison Barratt pp 8–9;
Tiffanie Beak pp 56–57;
Debbie Boon p 5;
Abigail Conway pp 42–43;
Graham Cox pp 26–29;
Paul Dainton pp 10–11;
Rosamund Fowler pp 54–55;
Emma Garner pp 58–59;
Rebecca Gryspeerdt pp 60–61;

Andrew Hamilton pp 32–33;
Charlotte Hard pp 20–21;
Anna Hopkins pp 14–15, 50–51;
Rosalind Hudson pp 12–13;
Neal Layton pp 16–17;
John Leonti pp 34–35;
Alan Marks pp 48–49;
Tony Morris pp 30–31;
Rhian Nest James pp 24–25;
Steve Rigby pp 18–19;
Nick Schon pp 36–37;

Linda Schwab pp 46–47;
Gary Taylor pp 38–39;
Bee Willey pp 6–7, 52–53;
Amanda Wood pp 22–23.